The Reading Quiz Book

For much of his 40 years in Reading Adam Sowan has been part of an informal network of people who seek to demonstrate that the town is not just Anywhere: it has its own identity, history, life and culture. This, along with a lifelong interest in words and places, has led him to write a series of books on aspects of the town. He is an activist in Reading Civic Society.

The Reading Quiz Book

Adam Sowan

TWO
RIVERS
PRESS

First published in the UK in 2012 by Two Rivers Press

7 DENMARK ROAD, READING RG1 5PA
www.tworiverspress.com

ISBN 978-1-901677-76-8

British Library Cataloguing in Publication Data. A catalogue record for this book is available
from the British Library.

2 3 4 5 6 7 8 9

Two Rivers Press is represented in the UK by Inpress Ltd and distributed by Central Books.

Cover design and lettering by Nadja Guggi and Geoff Sawers.
Text design by Nadja Guggi and typeset in Parisine.

Printed and bound in Great Britain by Imprint Digital, Exeter.

Contents

This quiz is intended to be neither too easy nor too hard: it's not much fun if you know all or none of the answers. I hope you enjoy guessing or researching, and maybe learn something from the further information which I have attached to many of the answers.

A warning: I didn't want to make this a purely historical quiz, so some questions relate to Reading as it is at the time of writing, in 2011. Things will inevitably change, and some answers will become less true.

A request: if you find something I have got wrong, please let me know via Two Rivers Press.

The section openers are illustrated with excerpts from The Ancient Boundary of Reading Map created by Geoff Sawers and Adam Stout. It is published by and available in poster form from Two Rivers Press.

... that ... Manor ... Did ... the Firs ... later ... been ... it's ...

THE M... a tale of th... dary at COLEY ... to the disgust ... nturies owned ... the Abbot...

ARCHITECTURE

was ...CKED perhaps PICKET ...e fence.

The boundary here divided two ancient estates. It must have ...en quite a ...sh-point ...ring the ...Civil War, for King

Vach... from can... killed a mon... bridge. He was forc... country — an incident that... the family motto, 'TIS BETTER TO SUFFER THAN TO REVENGE'.

Later Perambulators had problems too, but in 1687 Mayor Pococke "and all the rest went through the hall and orchard there without any interruption."

Things improved: in 1821 "the gentlemen were invited to partake of an elegant cold collation"

Sir Thomas Vachel of SOUTHCOTE
Sir Charles was a guest of DANIEL BLAGRAVE
while at Coley Park

(Wensley Rd)

⊗ a boundary ELM once stood here

In 1861 the line here went "right through a field of mangel wurzels"

COLEY MEAD now usually called KENNET MEADOW

OSIER BED

...of the ...called ...ejoins ...erties: ...Wash ...ter.

...y once

...RNETTS' MEADOW - a field ...cheekily took Southcote...

...peo...it th...cows on...lihol...There have...Read...heir...

1. Which of these buildings won a Civic Trust Award?

- ☐ King's Point
- ☐ John Lewis
- ☐ The Prudential building

King's Point

John Lewis

The Prudential building

2. Match the buildings with their Victorian designers:

1 The Abbey Gateway
2 Caversham Park
3 Reading School
4 St James's RC church

__ **A** Horace Jones
__ **B** Augustus Welby Northmore Pugin
__ **C** George Gilbert Scott
__ **D** Alfred Waterhouse

3. The Pevsner Architectural Guide to Berkshire has some unusual descriptions of buildings; match them up:

1 An angular beetle with a leaden carapace
2 A garrulous design
3 Glassy and glossy
4 A postmodern monster
5 Pragmatism and fantasy weirdly mixed

__ **A** Apex Plaza
__ **B** The Blade
__ **C** The Hexagon
__ **D** McIlroys, Oxford Road
__ **E** The University's Great Hall

Apex Plaza

The Blade

The Hexagon

McIlroys, Oxford Road

The University's Great Hall

4. The Soane obelisk in Market Place: which Isle did the stone come from?

☐ Portland
☐ Thanet
☐ Wight

Soane obelisk

High Bridge

5. The High Bridge: who designed it?

☐ Robert Adam
☐ Robert Brettingham
☐ John Soane

THE ARTS
& ENTERTAINMENT

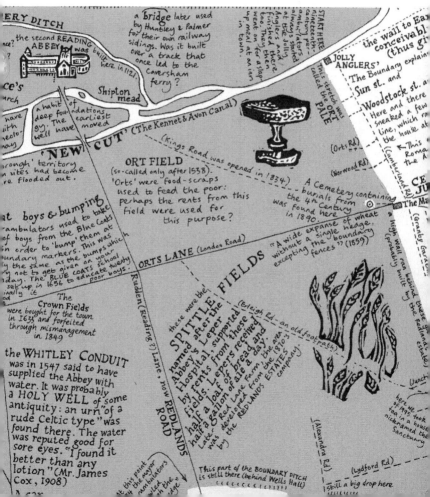

6. A famous writer lost the manuscript of a famous book on Reading station. Was it

- ☐ Enid Blyton's 'The Secret Seven'
- ☐ William Empson's 'Seven Types of Ambiguity'
- ☐ T E Lawrence's 'Seven Pillars of Wisdom'?

7. Which now-famous actor appeared in 'The Drunkard' at Progress Theatre in 1977?

8. What became of the independent Glendale cinema in Caversham?

- ☐ A bingo hall
- ☐ A church
- ☐ A pub

9. Which work of art on show in Reading depicts 33 buildings, 36 dogs, 37 ships, 190 horses and 626 human beings?

10. What links the following film directors with Reading: John and Roy Boulting, Sir David Lean, Karel Reisz?

CIVIC MATTERS

a well-heeled hilltop
...ining about paying rates to
...tween the Borough Boundary a...
...nce been WHITLEY PARK, private
...cluded fishponds, pleasure grounds
is probably on the site and is

~ now chr...

LES
EEN ~

...oundaries
awesome pl...
of dispute, riv...
and separation o...
but also places o...
meeting... Wit...
the DEAD also,
buried on boundarie...
in some splendour,
places both awesome
and central, as a
churchyard, a place to
connect with ancestors
...most important
...can be used to separate
people, that
are the boundaries
between

Territorial boundaries
between friends, between
parents and children, but...
to define or guard
to create an individual and
but also used to separate
can be
a sense of SELF
strangers on a train,
above all between
lovers

Once defined a
community's life:
source of food, people
and values... SPACE
defined.
protected. safe.
known.
secure.

MARK: an old Teutonic
word... meant 'country' or
'mark') as well.

s Not

GARDEN: an
enclosed
place, prot-
-ected, guarded.
EDEN and
the tree of
life were
guarded by cherubim
and the garden of the
Hesperides by a serpent
or a dragon

11. When was Reading Civic Society founded?

☐ 1937
☐ 1961
☐ 1974

12. How many places has Reading been twinned with?

13. Which four of these places are officially cities?

☐ Brighton and Hove
☐ Bury St Edmunds
☐ Chelmsford
☐ Guildford
☐ Leeds
☐ Milton Keynes
☐ Preston
☐ Southampton

14. Which two branch libraries celebrated their centenaries in 2007–8?

15. In 1911 a select committee of the House of Commons enquired into the proposal to bring Caversham into Reading. How many pages of minutes were there?

☐ 84
☐ 258
☐ 476

FOOD & DRINK

LOWER STREET

possible site of the ferry, built in 1238 with the help of King Henry III for the use of the pilgrims to the shrine of Our Lady.

DEANS FARM a very old site: a first-century Christian font was found in a well here.

EAST MEAD
later KINGS MEADOW

"not exceeded by any in England for Pleasure and Fertility" (1723) The western half was given to the town in 1875 but the eastern half was not.

gh the weir to a rowing boat

'T
Til
Whe
To a

a bridge later used by Huntley & Palmer for their own railway sidings. Was it built over a track that once led to the Caversham ferry?

nineteenth-century per-ambulators always started at the Jolly Anglers and finished there too. They then went on for a slap-up meal at an inn in town.

START HERE

ING as built here in 1121.

Shipton mead

JOLI
AN

ations arliest moved

Kennet & Avon Canal)

This stretch w called the ORT PALE

16. **Which Reading pub has served over 6500 different real ales since 1993?**

17. **Which pub threatened, in 1975, to defy new equality laws and maintain its 'ladies only' bar?**

18. **Which restaurant and bar brews its own beer?**

19. **How many Wetherspoon pubs are there in Reading?**

    ☐ One
    ☐ Two
    ☐ Three
    ☐ Four

20. **Where was the first ever Little Chef?**

    ☐ Basingstoke Road
    ☐ Shepherds Hill
    ☐ Calcot

21. **Simonds' brewery ran a house magazine from the 1920s to the 60s. What was its title?**

    ☐ The Barrel Organ
    ☐ The Hop Leaf Gazette
    ☐ The Quart-erly Review

22. Bel and the Dragon: what was the original purpose of the building?

Bel and the Dragon

23. Which four of these pubs or hotels were trading under their present names in 1830?

☐ Blagrave Arms, Blagrave Street
☐ Bugle, Friar Street
☐ Fisherman's Cottage, Kennetside
☐ Griffin, Caversham
☐ Horn, St Mary's Butts
☐ New Inn, Oxford Road
☐ Red Cow, Crown Street

MISCELLANEOUS

BROKEN BROW Wharf a... control of... of the... Kenne... conveniently allo... Dreadnoug... SOUNDA... bur...

later used

et & Avon Canal)

gs Road was opened in 1834)
...ter 1538.)
d-scraps
the poor:
rents from this
used for
purpose?

(Orts Rd.)

(Norwood Rd.)

The ... Sun st. and Woodstock st. are so ... Here and there the builders sneaked a few feet over the line, which ran right through the house at no 1 Norwood Rd.

← This could be a branch Roman Road, linking a Wharf where the Anglers is to the main St. Albans- Silchester route.

BUR... and ... 5th/6th cent... here in 1891.)

Reading in 1840

A Cemetery containing burials from the 4th Century was found here in 1890

CEMETERY JUNCTION

The Marquis of Granby, formerly the Gallows Tavern.

Crossroads boundarie were con spots for gall...

...NE (London Road)

...ITTLE FIELDS

"A wide expanse of wheat without a single hedge, excepting the boundary fences" (1859)

...y after the ...y's Leper
...spital supported
rents from these
...ields. Lepers received
half a loaf of bread and
half a gallon of ale a day.
Later ... Red Lane Farm the area
was developed from the 1910-31
by the REDLANDS ESTATES
Company.

(Erleigh Rd. — an old footpath)

↑ High wall ran behind these gardens (probably built by the Redlands estate)

(Granby Gardens)

(Eastern Avenue)

Wokingham Road, once Forest Road. (WINDSOR FOREST began at Loddon Bridge.

This was Hawthorne Field in 1669 and probably took its name from the boundary hedge, which followed a stream from WHITEKNIGHTS. By 1861 it had become much overgrown, but the man with the Mace got through, "to great personal inconvenience and occasionally some danger, but to the corresponding delight of the crowd."

(Junction Rd.)

here we took ... of 1995 tea in a house nicknamed the Sanctuary

(Alexandra Rd.)

(Foxhill Rd.)
(Cardigan Rd.)

a track

...es between ... houses

This part of the BOUNDARY DITCH is still there (behind Wells Hall)

(Lydford Rd.)

still a big drop here

(Upper Redlands Rd.)

Here ... stood the first Foxhill House. A Champagne breakfast from the owners for the perambulators of 1874.

...have ... alley behind Sutton walk

a boundary mark, ...settle and ... the thin fole Aubrey, quoting the ... (1000, Exodus ... word (Geol.) xxiii, 23)

...nark, ... or division, Pook: a boundary ...

The Marquis of Blandford planted an avenue of trees along here in 1798 as part of a drive around Whiteknights Park, which he owned

CORP OF D...

...christchurch Green

BEYOND THE PALE
.. outside the norm and out of bounds.
Rivers are natural boundaries but ... are also used ... everyone ... lite...

24. **When was Reading's first newspaper founded, and what was its name?**

25. **What were Albert, Fancy Rout, Button Nuts, Rich Travellers, Diadem, Brown College, and Thin Captain?**

26. **What type of deer live in the cemetery at Cemetery Junction?**

    ☐ Fallow
    ☐ Muntjac
    ☐ Red
    ☐ Roe

27. **How much does a resident of Reading have to pay per annum to use the University library for reference?**

    ☐ Nothing
    ☐ £40
    ☐ £80

28. A lot of people have said and written a lot of things about Reading. Match the quotes with their perpetrators:

1 A very large and wealthy town, handsomely built, the inhabitants rich and driving a very great trade.

2 But once arrived in Reading the enchantment is gone. A soporific atmosphere takes command, brought about by enervation, which in turn is ordered by the tranquillity of the river as it drains away with it the energies of the people.

3 I always said, and you were always in a passion when I said it, that the Reading coach people, the Reading post people, and Reading altogether, was the most careless, blundering, unpunctual town ever heard of.

4 I am delighted with the people that I have seen at Reading.

5 People avoid Reading but even the streets of terracotta shops and houses in the centre of town have a good deal to be said for them when you know them in different lights.

6 Reading looks pretty much like any other town. There's a Timothy White's and Woolworths.

7 This is truly a town of meeting: of the waters of rivers, and of these friends in a place kept tidy for the spirit of Jesus Christ.

__ **A** William Cobbett, 1822
__ **B** Daniel Defoe, 1724
__ **C** Charles Dickens, 1843
__ **D** Mary Russell Mitford, 1813
__ **E** John Peel, 1990
__ **F** John Piper, 1939
__ **G** William Penn, 1705

NAMES

as

X

once w...
'Clerks

WELL
MAN'S F...
the Ab...

Kings'
the boundar...
the middle o...
was borne h...
(as the ...
water
the

△ buried a cone in concrete

the LAND MEAD now 'WATERLOO MEADOWS'

Elgar (P.)

WATERLOO BRICK KILN (Swain-stone rd.) source of much of Vic-torian Readings' brickwork

still a highwall here

later CUT-THROAT LANE

marker

St Shin...
est...

Whitley Grove, a nineteenth-century villa straddled the line at this point. 'the ho-use is outside the line while the kitchen is within it.

PERRINS LANE

In 1861 'the garden was trampled on by the invaders.'

broken 'over-run and filled up' (still) within...

un-avoidable

The 1874 Perambu-lators crossed the Kennet in a large ballast-boat. One of them fell in, head first, 'to the delight of the sightseers.' If you haven't got a boat ready and don't much fancy swimming, follow the footpath to the new bridge here.

Basingstoke Road

site of Rose's Kilns

Psalm 104 was recommended reading during the Rogationtide Perambu-lations for the bounty of the earth -lations ~ a prayer of thanks-giving for banishing the in general and for FLOOD in parti-waters of the HAST SET A BO... cular. 'THOU MAY NOT P... OVER, THEY the solid wor... (v.9) ~ a boundar between humankind and t... boundless prim... chaos of the

29. Several writers have invented fictional names for Reading; match them:

1 Aldbrickham
2 Belford Regis
3 Norley

__ **A** Thomas Hardy
__ **B** Mary Russell Mitford
__ **C** Elizabeth Taylor

30. What was a Reading tallboy?

☐ A chimney-pot
☐ An item of furniture made by Elliotts
☐ A cocktail invented in the 1960s at the George hotel?

31. What is or was the Reading Rota?

☐ A 13th-century song
☐ A 1920s fairground ride
☐ A corrupt 18th-century voting system

32. What resort was known as Reading-by-Sea?

☐ Hayling Island
☐ Lee-on-the-Solent
☐ Weston-Super-Mare

33. In which Shakespeare play is Reading mentioned?

PEOPLE

...CE: they ... out at 8½ ...alking in 'Chronicle' ...ly twenty

Peram... round (clock... widdershi... but

...aduus ...

...report ...miles'. ...one, in a physica... view, he panted.

Wilmington is an ancient

now Oxford Rd

SLAPSTICK AND PRACTICAL JOKE... -ambulations. In 1874 they left th... "sky-larking", - pushing the perambulators into and muddy ditches, with various other rude jokes, allowable only on such occasions, were not less than thirty persons a... being in a ditch, most of them rolling very altered characters. up to a rather fatiguing although amusing T... day.

In 1844 they got up... to the boundary-bea...

Here in ...RENCE bailiff bu ST. EDMUND an for himself. He wa

practical affording 'There emerging time, added

PEGGS Is also spelt PIGS- this may once have been an old drovers route

GS GREEN LANE

two WYVERNS once guarded the to COLEY PARK.

Cast

MURDERED MONK ...le of the border ~

COLEY PARK went through the ...disgust of the Vachel ...owned it. One

Avenue

34. What does the statue of George Palmer in Palmer Park hold in his right hand?

☐ A bible
☐ A tin of biscuits
☐ A top hat and an umbrella

35. In Eldon Square there is a statue of Rufus Isaacs, Lord Reading; where was it originally erected?

36. Who lost his life in a whirlwind at Reading station in 1840?

☐ George East
☐ Leslie North
☐ Caleb South
☐ Henry West

37. Who was Father Willis?

☐ The builder of the Town Hall's organ
☐ An eccentric vicar of St Laurence's in the 1890s
☐ A tramp who lived under Reading Bridge in the 1930s

38. Seven of these writers compiled histories of Reading. Which?

☐ The Rev Charles Coates
☐ Dr W M Childs
☐ Charles Dickens
☐ P H Ditchfield
☐ J Doran
☐ Ernest Dormer
☐ Michael Hinton
☐ Stuart Hylton
☐ John Man
☐ Mary Russell Mitford
☐ Leslie North
☐ Daphne Phillips
☐ Adam Sowan

39. The Oxford Dictionary of National Biography lists 413 people who had some connexion with Reading; among them are the following. Match the names with their occupations.

1 Adeliza
2 Daniel Blagrave
3 The Marquis of Blandford
4 Edith Julia Morley
5 Thomas Noon Talfourd

__ **A** Bibliophile and gardener
__ **B** Judge, Member of Parliament and playwright
__ **C** Member of Parliament and regicide
__ **D** Professor and suffragette
__ **E** Queen

40. Whose memorial in St Laurence's bears the words Cubus, Tetraedron, Octaedron, Dodecaedron and Icosaedron?

41. Who was Laurenthes Braag, whose memorial is attached to the south wall of St Mary's?

☐ A Belgian chemist who worked for the photographer W H Fox-Talbot

☐ A Danish merchant seaman who died while on parole as a prisoner of war in 1808

☐ A Dutch soldier killed in the Reading Skirmish of 1688

42. Where are both Huntley and Palmer buried?

☐ The Friends' Meeting House

☐ St Mary's churchyard

☐ Reading Cemetery

43. Match these Reading-related people with their nicknames:

1 William Laud
2 William Henry Tee
3 Richard Valpy

__ **A** Little Hocus-pocus
__ **B** The Mighty Flogger
__ **C** Mr Reading

44. Why is Mr Barratt's memorial in Reading Cemetery made of iron?

George Barratt's memorial

45. Which monarchs gave their names to King's Meadow, King's Road and King Street?

46. Whose coronation is depicted on a capital from Reading Abbey, now displayed in the Museum of Reading?

☐ King Henry I
☐ King John
☐ The Blessed Virgin Mary

on Plinths
the entrance
PARK.

...ning
...ng

cloth

...d eye
...riegat
(with
...in br...
...ters ro...

...e did not become a
...h route until 1911)

≪A favourite beauty
'Here the swain wit
The cheerful land...
The rising hill, en...
And vales, where

OYSTER-S...
once foun...
in vast p...
puzzled
experts
Robert
though
be t
a

EY was rebuilt

became COLEY
...me buildings
...ECOTE
...resque
...ss

Bobs
Mount

...e recommend
...ck the route of
...NCH LINE. It didn't
...ailway line (1908-
...akes for a fine and
...lk today... but
... call it cheating; the
... be the first; the
...adhered strictly to the
...ry, but many others
...at nearest points, making
...ts. (1874)

once
known
as
Kennet
Moor

site of th...
WATERLOO
BRICK KIL...
source of
much of V...
torian
Readings
brickwork

the
LAND
MEAD
now
WATERLOO
MEADOWS

(Elgar)

but unavoidable

points, making

The 1874
Perambu-
lators
crossed
the K...

PERRINS
...line
...use...
...kitchen...
in 1861 the...
...well fram...

47. The Great Expectations pub, London Street.
Name some former uses this building has had.

The Great Expectations Pub

48. Where is the longest continuous terrace of houses in Reading?

- ☐ Elgar Road
- ☐ Gosbrook Road
- ☐ Liverpool Road

49. How long is Reading's High Street?

- ☐ 40 metres
- ☐ 120 metres
- ☐ 480 metres

50. What do the following streets have in common?
Junction Road (Reading), Rectory Road (Caversham),
Polstead Road (Tilehurst)?

51. Why was Battle Hospital so called?

- ☐ It was first built in 1644 to deal with casualties from the Civil War
- ☐ It was built on land once belonging to Battle Abbey in Sussex
- ☐ It was endowed by Sir Edward Battell of Tilehurst

52. Where in Reading is there an award-winning roof-garden?

- ☐ The Ibis Hotel
- ☐ John Lewis
- ☐ Reading International Solidarity Centre

53. Where is the only right-to-roam access land in Reading?

- ☐ Clayfield Copse
- ☐ The Cowsey
- ☐ View Island

54. How many museums are there in Greater Reading?

- ☐ Three
- ☐ Five
- ☐ Seven

55. What is the official name of Smelly Alley?

56. Which of the following are

- **A** wholly within Reading Borough
- **B** partly in and partly out
- **C** wholly outside?

- __ **1** BBC Listening Centre, Caversham Park
- __ **2** Madejski Stadium
- __ **3** Mapledurham playing fields
- __ **4** Reading University's Whiteknights campus
- __ **5** Savacentre, Calcot
- __ **6** The Shire Hall, Whitley Wood Lane
- __ **7** Thames Valley Business Park

57. The Lion in the Forbury Gardens. What colour is he painted?

- ☐ Afghan Sable
- ☐ Burnt Umber
- ☐ Invisible Green

The Lion in the Forbury Gardens

Footbridge at Kennetmouth

58. The footbridge attached to the Great Western railway bridge at Kennetmouth. What is its unofficial name?

ntre of pilgrimage. Its'
luded the head of the
christ on the Cross and spear
— WING' said

RELIGION

his year

The Mace was passed through the w...
into a rowing
Caversham Lock

EAST M
later
KINGS MEA

Bridge
-omer (1923)

"not exceeded by a
for Pleasure and
The western half
the town in 1875
eastern half

THE PLUMMERY DITCH

a bridge later u
by Huntley & Palm
for their own railw
sidings. Was it buil
over a track tha
once led to the
Caversham
ferry?

Forbury
Hill
Civil War defence?
King Stephen's
castle?
a tumulus?

the second READING
ABBEY was built
here in 1121.

■St.Laurence's
the Abbey church

Shipton
mead

ich would have
Finally the
centre of
led 'the

a habit of
deep fou-ndations
gy. The earliest
well have moved

others, for towns have
their own pasts, with
destroy the archeolo-
settlements may

'NEW CUT' (The Kennet & Avo

(Kings Roa

around the 'borough' territory
anyway. when sites had become
'sour' or were flooded out.

ORT FIELD
(so-called only after 153
'Orts' were food-scr
used to feed the
perhaps the rents
field were used
this pur

Blue Coat boys & bumping
Civic Perambulators used to take
the Blue Coats
at

LONDON
Friar st
la

59. **Where in Reading can you see a Victorian rood screen originally installed in St Chad's cathedral, Birmingham?**

    ☐ Holy Trinity church
    ☐ Reading Museum
    ☐ Reading School chapel

60. **What was the dedication of the Abbey church?**

    ☐ St John the Baptist and The Blessed Virgin Mary
    ☐ St James the Greater
    ☐ St James the Less

61. **Reading Abbey had a 'daughter' priory in a town in Herefordshire, which also has a Forbury. Name the town.**

62. **Which other sect worships at St Bartholomew's Anglican church?**

63. **A mummified hand, found in the Abbey ruins, was supposed to have been that of St James. Where is it now kept?**

    ☐ Reading Museum
    ☐ A church in Marlow
    ☐ The Vatican

... royal Fores...
the Abbot o...
Reading had
of 'wa...
sm...

...ent times: perhaps
town boundary
...ked the point at
...h the fields stopped
...the Forest began.

... area
... wooded until

...ITH

...AWAY,

...s of
...ading's
...hdea-
...n but
...ulti~
...the
...n
...out

...ion-

...a

...GLES,
...lds in a

(Wilson)

(Wantage)

(Waverley Rd)

(1996 - 1998)

...lves 'trudging
over a ploughed
field.' We of 1995, glad
to be back in the
terraced streets again,
ran into friends, and
took refreshment in
the SPREAD EAGLE.

round

elm park

Prospect Park

once owned by the feisty
FRANCES KENDRICK,
who challenged a man
to fight her or to marry
her. She won, and they
built a house in the
woods that eventually
became the 'MANSION HOUSE'
of today.
Originally it was called
DIRLES FARM — from DOLE,?
meaning division or boundary?

LOVE LANE long since gone,
but the wall behind
these properties follows the line

(parkside Rd.) except for this end

Outside this old
lodge to Prospect Park
there is still a **Boundary**
Stone, put up by the parish
St. Mary. (it was their bound
too.) A Bluecoat boy wa...
'bumped' here by the
heartless perambula...

to ...
to ...
the ...
The ...
gra...
me...
area
Bath R...

Tileh...

this
was
PYLE
FIELD

The lands...

field wa...

64. When was Reading Football Club founded?

- ☐ 1834
- ☐ 1871
- ☐ 1925
- ☐ 1947

65. In the 1978/9 season an RFC goalkeeper played for 1,103 minutes without conceding a goal. What was his name?

66. Every Easter a long-distance race passes through Reading. Where does it start and finish?

- ☐ Devizes and Westminster
- ☐ London and Bath
- ☐ Oxford and Southampton

...on plinths
...PARK. ...the entrance

Katesgrove
treasure - one
HAMOND CHASTELEY
received permission
...King to

...were bought
in 1635 and
through m...
in 1...

...ouse at COLEY was rebuilt
...the 1700's -
...old site became COLEY
...RM. Some buildings
...ive, a DOVECOTE
...and picturesque
...adows too, across

A Favourite ...
'Here, the sw...
The cheerf...
The rising ...
And vales...

...once found here
in vast profusion
puzzled the
experts for centuries...
Robert PLOT (1640-96)
thought they might
be the remains of
a Viking
banquet...

rude Ce...
found t...
was repu...
sore eye...
better f...
lotion"
Cox, 190...

A car
park
marks
the
spot.

X

Bobs
Mount

CLERKENWELL FIELD probably
later CLACKMAN'S FIELD
named after the Abbey conduit
opposite. (Clerks Well")

...me this way we recommend
...beaten track. The route of
...COLEY BRANCH LINE. It didn't
...s) but it makes for a fine and
...ling as a railway today.
...untrified walk today; the
Some might call it cheating; but
you won't be the first; the
officials adhered strictly to the
boundary, but many others
aimed at nearest points, making
short cuts. (1874)

once
known
as
Kennet
Moor

the
LAND
MEAD
now
WATERLOO
MEADOWS

site of the
WATERLOO
BRICK KILN (Swain-
stoned)
Source of
much of Vic-
torian
Readings'
brickwork

(Swain-
stoned)
still a high wall here

Kir...
the bow...
the mid...
was bo...
(as...

...marble...
...a cove in...
...concrete

later CUT-THROAT LANE

PERRINS LANE

"Whitley
Grove,' a
nineteenth-
century villa
straddled the
Point 'the ho-
use is along the
line while the
kitchen is within it'...

in 1861 (this
filled up with
pikes and
brambles and)
'over-run and
trampled on by the
invaders.'

The garden was

Basingstoke Road

The 1874
Parambu-
lators
crossed
the Kennet
in a large
ballast-boat.
One of them
fell in, head
first, 'to the
delight of the
sightseers.' If you
haven't got a boat
ready and don't much
fancy swimming, follow the
footpath to the new bridge
here.

GREAT
FOBNEY
COMMON
MEADOW
often
underwater

Rose Kiln Lane - noisy but unavoidable

...KAY'd

...flooding

...and it's
...air, cattle
grew... into

site
of
Rose's
Kilns

The Kennet - 'Reading River' (1669)
upon whose banks the town of Reading
grew, rises near Avebury in Wiltshire.

Psalm 104 was recommended reading
during the Rogationtide Perambu-
-lations ~ a prayer of thanks-
giving for the bounty of the earth
in general and for banishing
waters of the FLOOD in pa-
cular. 'THOU HAST SET A
OVER.' (v.9) MAY NO...
...between the solid
...humankind a...
...boundless p...
...haos of w...

67. Which shop used the Lamson pneumatic cash system?

☐ Eighteen's fishmongers
☐ Jackson's outfitters
☐ Vicars' butchers

68. Where was the Dolls' Hospital?

☐ Next to the chapel in the Royal Berks
☐ On the corner of Bridge Street and Castle Street
☐ In Tutty's toyshop

69. Name the two new hotels on Friar Street.

70. How many branches of Waterstones does Reading have?

☐ One
☐ Two
☐ Three
☐ Four

71. Who baked biscuits first, Huntley or Palmer?

72. Where did Suttons obtain their seeds?

☐ All over the world
☐ Earley
☐ The Floral Mile

73. Where was Simonds' first brewery?

☐ Bridge Street
☐ Broad Street
☐ Friar Street

74. Three more Bs: match the (long defunct) firms to their products:

1 Dymore Brown

2 Fidlers

3 Serpells

__ **A** Beer

__ **B** Biscuits

__ **C** Seeds

75. And these three Cs:

1 Cocks

2 Colliers

3 The Co-operative Wholesale Society

__ **A** Bricks

__ **B** Jam

__ **C** Sauce

TRANSPORT

BROKEN BROW

Wharf a...

...of the bo...

...ontrol of...

...the Kenn...

...conveniently allow...

...eadnought

...DARY

the concel... (thus giv...

...GLERS'

The Boundary explains why

Sun st. and

Woodstock st. are so short. Here and there the builders sneaked a few feet over the line, which ran right through the house at no 1 Norwood Rd.

←This could be a branch Roman Road, linking a wharf where the Anglers is to the main St. Albans – Silchester route.

both a...

such a...

to consider a...

cemetery site...

BURIAL and nine cremation

5th/6th century discovered

here in 1891.}

...e Great Western Railway reached Reading in 1840

(Cumberland Rd.)

(Rd.)

CEMETERY JUNCTION

containing

◉

wheat ge, ary)

The Marquis of Granby, formerly the Gallows Tavern.

(Granby Gardens)

(Eastern Avenue)

a high wall ran behind these gardens (probably built by the Redlands estate)

Crossroads and boundaries were common spots for gallows.

Wokingham Road, once Forest Road. (WINDSOR FOREST began at Loddon Bridge.)

This was Hawthorne Field in 1669 and probably took it's name from the boundary hedge, which followed a stream from WHITEKNIGHTS. By 1861 it had become much overgrown, but the man with the Mace ...rough, "to great personal ...d occasionally

...n Rd.)

A:

76. Within the borough there are a number of mileposts giving the distance to various points in London by various routes. Match them up.

1 35¾
2 40
3 58
4 68¼

_ **A** Charing Cross by train
_ **B** Hyde Park Corner by road
_ **C** Paddington by train
_ **D** Putney Bridge by bike

77. How many platforms did Reading station have in 2010?

☐ Six
☐ Eight
☐ Ten
☐ Twelve

78. How many railway locomotives have there been with 'Reading' in their name?

☐ One
☐ Three
☐ Five

79. Where did Reading's first stretch of turnpike road go?

☐ Maidenhead
☐ Oxford
☐ Puntfield

80. What is the number of the dual carriageway that links Sutton's Seeds Business Park with Winnersh Triangle?

☐ A329
☐ A329(M)
☐ A3290
☐ M329

81. Long-distance European footpath E2 passes through Reading; where does it start and finish?

☐ Cape Wrath to Syracuse
☐ Land's End to Istanbul
☐ Nice to Stranraer

82. Before the coming of the railways, towns kept their own time, not GMT. How far behind London time was Reading?

☐ 72 seconds
☐ 3¾ minutes
☐ 10 minutes

Reading Station

WATER

we recomm...
the route of...
it didn't...
...98-

the
LAND
MEAD
now
WATERL...
MEADOW

...well...
...e old COLEY...
last long as a rail...
1985) but it makes for...
...countrified walk today...
Some might call it cheatin...
you won't be the first: th...
officials adhered strictly to the... others
boundary, but many... making
aimed at nearest points,
short cuts. (1874)

The 187...
Perambu-
lators
crossed
the Kenne...
in a large
ballast-bo...
One of the...
fell in, hea...
first, to t...
delight of...
sightseers...
haven't g...
ready an...
fancy sw...
footpath t...
here.

...AY BRAYN KAY?
...often spelt
...ading

...vent flooding

**GREAT
FOBNEY
COMMON
MEADOW**
often
underwater

Rose Kiln Lane – noisy but unavoidable

...meadows, and it's
...ired their cattle
...ocessed into
...dieval

site
of
Rose's
Kilns

The Kennet – 'Reading River' (1669)
upon whose banks the town of Reading
grew, rises near Avebury in Wiltshire.

83. **Which watercourse has at various times been used for all these purposes? Drive a mill, fill a moat, supply water for steam locomotives, fill a swimming bath?**

   ☐ The Holy Brook
   ☐ The River Kennet
   ☐ The Portmanbrook

84. **How many navigable locks are there in the Borough?**

   ☐ Three
   ☐ Four
   ☐ Five

85. **Why do pedestrians not push this button?**

86. When did the Abbey Mill last grind?

- ☐ 1539
- ☐ 1798
- ☐ 1957

Abbey Mill

87. What flower, to be found growing at Kennetmouth, is named for another local river?

88. What listed structure in Reading can only be seen by getting your feet wet and using a torch?

89. Where does Reading's drinking water come from?

- ☐ The Kennet
- ☐ The Thames
- ☐ Wells sunk into the chalk

90. What are Appletree, Bohemian, Buck's, the Elephants' Graveyard, Fry's, Heron, Piper's, Poplar, St Mary's and View?

to half-way across the river

...ough the rest by boat, hiccups. In 1874 the boat went to Norcot Scou... mistake. The... more ...

...ambulators, ...oil

he MACE was to
Civic Perambulatio...
what the L...
...oot...

WHERE IS IT?

...ied along
...ambles and
...dows and walls. It was borne
ponds, passed through
rooftops...
Mace was the symbol of civic pomp
authority, and the mayors' right to
...ave one was wrested from the Abbot
...und 1460. Before then he had to
...ake do with "two tipped staffs"
ling
with

and very low-lying. In wet
years it can bec-ome a mud-
bath, as thousands of festival-goers
will tell you. "the rain had made the ground
in a very disagreeable state", complained
Perambulators of 1874, who for some reason
came this way in October. "Plan-ks would have
been useful for crossing the wa-ter courses, but
none were to be obtained, and consequently
all had to do their best by jumping.
which afforded much amusement!"

LITTLE JOHN'S FARM – a
newish name for an oldish
site.

NUMBERS: In 1861
the ex-mayor, the
serjents, most of th
Coats Boys and a t
up to 400 "volu
probably

(Portman Rd)

WILDS
F
HURST

...as once a
...ered hamlets
...f heath and
...NTWOOD
...ay have
...en
...me
...st,

(Chester St)

Perambulators regularly made
a PIT-STOP DETOUR to BATTLE
FARM (now Barnwood Close).
'Victuals, wine, and
strong liquors', no doubt!
went down well in 1729.

...like the Long
chalk hill figure
Man of Wilmington on the
ancient Sussex Downs

Cow Lane

DISTANCE: they
worked it out at 8½
miles of land walking in
1874, but in 1861 the Chronicle
reporter put it at 'nearly 9
miles'. The duty is an excee
one, in a physical point of
view, he panted

BATTLE WORKHOUSE
(later Battle Hospital)
opened in 1867. Some
buildings straddled the
Line. In 1874 and 1884
windows were officially
broken to make way
for the Mace.

an Anglo-Saxon
warrior was buried
here with a spear
and his head
covered by
his shield

(Beresford Rd)

SLAPSTICK AND PRACTICAL JOKES
ambulations. In 1874 they le
of a wall, and in 1844 – pushing
'sky-larking', ...
and muddy ditches.
jokes allowable an
vast amusement
'There were not less
time, rolling in
emerging
being
added

The weary Perambulators
of 1874 here found
themselves 'trudging
over a ploughed
field. We of 1945, glad
to be back in the
terraced streets again,
ran into friends and
took refreshment in
the SPREAD EAGLE.

(Wantage Rd)

PANGBOURNE LANE now Oxford Rd

The
Manor of
BATTLE
was one of many
given by William I
to Battle Abbey in thanks
to God for letting him win
the Battle of Hastings.
The name Battle
gradually came to
mean the whole
area between the
Bath Road and the river.

PEGGS:
...also spelt Pigs-
this is why anyone could
have been an
old drovers mute

(Bath Rd)

elm park
...pect Park
by the feisty
KENDRICK
...ged a man
...or to marry
...and they
...e in the
...ntually
...sion

(1866–1888)

LOVE
(Rd)

Tilehurst Road was
once called
PYLE
...this
...was
...FIELD

PEGGS GREEN LANE

...NK

91

92

93

94

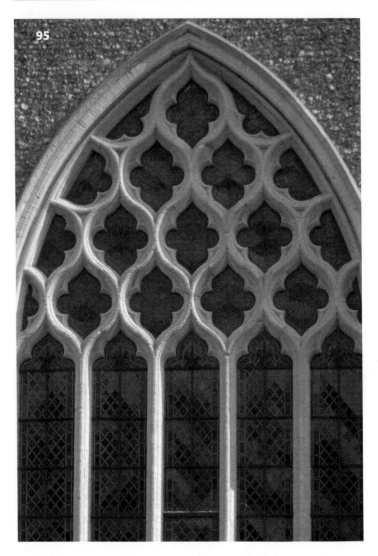

95

96

97

98

99

100

101

102

103

104

105

106

107

108

109

110

BATTLE MEAD

and very low-lying. In wet years it co...

in at...
ale laid o...
fo...
in 1729

...ors of 1874, who for some reason ...vay in October. "Plan-ks would have for crossing the wa-ter courses, but to be obtained, and consequently do their best by jumping. ...ded much amusement!"

(Richfield Avenue)

NUMBERS: In 1861 The Mayor, the... the ex-mayor, the Mace-bearers, th... Serjents, most of the Corporation, half... Coats Boys and a team of Labourer... up to 400 "volunteers" for the d... probably make quite a me...

Cow Lane

DISTANCE: they worked it out at 8½ miles of land walking in 1874, but in 1861 the 'Chronicle' reporter put it at 'nearly twenty miles'. The duty is an exceedingly arduous one, in a physical point of view, he panted.

DIRECTION: For... Perambulato... round... wi...

Man of Wilmington a who guards an ancient boundary on the Sussex Downs.

SLAPSTICK AND PRACTICAL JOKES were a feature o... ...ambulations. In 1874 they left a police-searg... and in 1844 they got up to 'the... - pushing the perambulators... 'sky-larking' - with various other... and muddy ditches, only on such occa... jokes, allowable amusement to the boundar... vast not less than thirty per... were rolling in a ditch, most of... being very altered char... up to a rather fat... although amusing... day.

LANE now Oxford Rd

...ractical ...ffording ...time, ...rging ...dded

ST. ED... for himse...

ARCHITECTURE

1 King's Point, in 1969, when it was called Alpha House. It is now reviled as Reading's worst eyesore.

2 1C, 2A, 3D, 4B. The original 13th-century Abbey Gate collapsed from neglect in 1861. Caversham Park is an early iron-framed building, put up in 1851 for ironmaster William Crawshay. Waterhouse lived at Foxhill, now on the University campus, and designed many buildings in Reading. Pugin was a Gothic Revivalist, but this early work is Neo-Norman.

3 1C, 2E, 3B, 4A, 5D. The revisers of the 2010 edition have emulated Pevsner's often quirky turns of phrase.

4 Portland. This stone was widely used in London; the obelisk was erected in 1804, before the canal opened up supplies of Bath stone in 1810.

5 Robert Brettingham, although Soane's name was suggested. Built in 1788, just before the canal was thought of, it has been a bottleneck ever since.

ANSWERS

THE ARTS & ENTERTAINMENT

6 Lawrence's 'Seven Pillars'; he had to rewrite the whole thing from memory.

7 Kenneth Branagh, playing a well-off young man who goes to the bad in this Victorian melodrama. Progress were celebrating the opening of their licenced bar.

8 The New Testament Church of God. The Glendale showed a mixture of films, some arty and some saucy.

9 The replica Bayeux Tapestry in the Museum of Reading. Like the original, it is strictly embroidery, not tapestry. Only a handful of the humans are female.

10 They all received part of their education in the town. Other cinematic links are: Bugsy Malone, partly filmed in the abandoned Huntley & Palmers factory; Robinson in Space, which starts with scenes showing Reading Mainline's short-lived Routemaster bus services; and Ricky Gervais's Cemetery Junction, which has little to do with Reading.

CIVIC MATTERS

11 1961. Many other Civic Societies arose around this time, prompted by the terrible architecture of the era and national concerns such as the destruction of the Euston Arch. Slough, however, was way in front; the formation of its society in 1937 may have been not unconnected with John Betjeman's famous couplet: 'Come, friendly bombs, and fall on Slough/It isn't fit for humans now.'

12 Six, although some twinnings were less than formal: Düsseldorf, Germany; Clonmel, Ireland; San Francisco Libre, Nicaragua; Zaandam, Netherlands; Armidale, Australia; Speightstown, Barbados. Düsseldorf was one of the first post-war links with an 'enemy' city; Zaandam was mainly a sporting exchange; in 1977 Armidale asked to be twinned with 'a rural English town', but nothing much came of it. Reading has more Barbadians than anywhere outside Barbados.

13 Brighton and Hove, Leeds, Preston, Southampton. None of them have cathedrals. Reading has made several unsuccessful bids for city status.

14 Battle and Caversham, both built with the help of the Scottish-American philanthropist Andrew Carnegie.

15 476. One witness said: 'You cannot go over to Caversham but you meet Reading men, one after the other, with smiling faces looking all the better for living in Caversham but earning their living in Reading.'

ANSWERS

FOOD AND DRINK

16 The Ale House, formerly the Hobgoblin and before that the London Tavern.

17 The Butler, Chatham Street. 'Ladies' Bar' was etched into a window.

18 Zero Degrees, Bridge Street, very close to the site of the old Simonds'/Courage brewery.

19 Four: The Baron Cadogan in Caversham, The Hope Tap, The Monks' Retreat, and The Back of Beyond; this last went smokeless well before the national ban.

20 Basingstoke Road. It opened in 1958, with just 11 seats.

21 The Hop Leaf Gazette. The editor had suggested the other two names. Reading Library has a complete run of the Gazette; its pages show what generous and caring employers the Simonds family were.

22 Pumping sewage: from the then (1873) lowest point in the borough, through a pipe laid in the bed of the Kennet, to Manor Farm sewage works. It was powered by the river itself by way of a turbine. An electric pump on the site now does the job.

23 Griffin, Horn, New Inn, Red Cow; the second and fourth are still in their original buildings.

MISCELLANEOUS

24 1723: The Reading Mercury and Weekly Entertainer, one of the first local papers in the country. In the early years the news was almost entirely from London, and only the adverts were local.

25 Huntley and Palmers' biscuits. These and many others are listed in several rhyming stanzas of a poem written in 1891 by J Mosdell, village carrier of Mortimer.

26 Muntjac; they are not very shy.

27 Nothing.

28 1B, 2C, 3D, 4A, 5F, 6E, 7G. A very mixed press.

NAMES

29 1A, 2B, 3C. Hardy, in Jude the Obscure, found surprisingly little gloom or doom in the town; our own Miss Mitford was polite about it in her book; Taylor's eponymous heroine Angel found it 'hateful'.

30 A chimney-pot; at up to 7'6" they were among the longest made anywhere.

31 A 13th-century song, the famous round 'Sumer is Icumen in'. The manuscript was found in the Abbey records; its complexity put Reading in the vanguard of musical development.

32 Hayling Island. As the nearest bit of seaside, it was most popular as a coach trip destination after WWII; for many years it had a holiday home for the elderly called Reading House.

33 The Merry Wives of Windsor, Act IV, Scene V. It's an incidental mention in a laboured joke which is not worth trying to explain. The name is spoken by a stage Welshman who pronounces it 'Redins'.

PEOPLE

34 A top hat and an umbrella. The sculptor was criticised for giving him unpressed trousers. Palmer has been joined by the great French actor and film director Jacques Tati, whose brolly-wielding statue stands in Saint-Maur-des-Fosses, Paris.

35 New Delhi. It was moved in 1971.

36 Henry West; a memorial board in St Laurence's churchyard records the event, a week before the line opened.

37 The organ builder. The instrument, widely admired, has kept its character as a grand Victorian concert organ.

38 Coates (1802), Childs (1905, 'a first sketch for children'), Doran (1835), Hinton (1954), Hylton (2007), Man (1816), Phillips (1999).

39 1E, 2C, 3A, 4D, 5B. Adeliza was Henry I's second wife, and came to the dedication of his tomb in the Abbey. Blagrave signed Charles I's death warrant. Morley was the first female professor in the country.

40 John Blagrave, mathematician, who died in 1611. The words are the five regular solids in geometry.

41 A Danish PoW. These involuntary visitors were well-treated and well-liked.

42 The Friends' Meeting House, with humble gravestones in this peaceful oasis.

43 1A, 2C, 3B. Archbishop Laud, born in Reading, was short of stature and had many enemies. Tee was a long-serving Town Clerk. Valpy ruled over Reading School for almost 50 years.

44 He owned an ironworks in town.

45 Henry VIII, William IV, George III respectively.

46 The BVM; this is the earliest known depiction of this event.

PLACES

47 Scientific Institution, Methodist Chapel, Theatre, Newspaper office.

48 Liverpool Road.

49 40 metres; possibly the shortest in the land.

50 They, or parts of them, are subject to Article 4 Directions, which give greater protection than Conservation Areas. Reading's 14 Directions are intended mainly to preserve examples of the famous patterned brickwork from stone-cladders.

51 Battle Abbey land.

52 RISC. The garden is open for charity occasionally.

53 The Cowsey, a little-known open space and wildlife habitat off Blagdon Road in Whitley.

54 Seven: the Museum of Reading, Blake's Lock, the Medical Museum at the Royal Berkshire Hospital, the Museum of English Rural Life, the Museum of Berkshire Aviation at Woodley and, on the University campus, the Cole Museum of Zoology and the Ure Museum of Greek Archaeology.

55 Union Street.

56 1A, 2A, 3A, 4B, 5C, 6C, 7C. Reading's boundaries are wayward to a degree.

57 Invisible Green, a very dark colour invented for Regency park railings; black would have been too much of a contrast with the shrubbery. The Lion has always had to be painted because he is made of rustable cast iron, not bronze. The Duke of Sutherland's private railway carriage in the museum at York is also Invisible Green.

58 The Horseshoe Bridge.

ANSWERS

RELIGION

59 Holy Trinity Church; as the new Pevsner Guide says, it is full of fittings 'garnered by the late Canon Brian Brindley from redundant or unappreciative churches'.

60 St John the Baptist and the BVM.

61 Leominster.

62 The Greek Orthodox community, who dedicate it to St Elias.

63 A Roman Catholic church in Marlow. The hand was briefly on show at St James's church, Reading, on his Feast day in 2011.

SPORT

64 1871; the first match, played against Reading School on King's Meadow, ended in a goalless draw.

65 Steve Death.

66 Devizes and Westminster. It's a gruelling 125-mile canoe race on the Kennet and Avon and the Thames, first rowed in 1948; the record stands at 15 hours 34 minutes. By the time they reach Reading the boats are rather strung out; watch them doing portage in front of the Fisherman's Cottage pub.

TRADE & INDUSTRY

67 Jacksons. Your £20 notes were whooshed down a tube in a canister to the cashier's office in the basement, and your change was whisked back up. This was believed to be the last example of the system still in commercial use until the shop closed in 2013.

68 Bridge Street and Castle Street.

69 Ibis and Novotel. The architect evidently thought that the blue upper stories would blend with the sky, so that we would fail to notice how disastrously out-of-scale the whole edifice was.

70 Two: one in the Oracle and the other in the splendid former Broad Street Chapel.

71 Huntley, in London Street; he bowed out fairly early, but the Palmers loyally kept his name in the company title until the end.

72 All over the world; the Reading operation packed, tested and sorted.

73 Broad Street.

74 1A, 2C, 3B.

75 1C, 2A, 3B.

TRANSPORT

76 1C, 2B, 3D, 4A. The bikeway follows the Thames towpath; Charing Cross was reached (slowly) via Guildford, Redhill and Croydon. Well into the 1960s there was a through train from London Bridge to Reading by this route.

77 Twelve: 1–10 plus 4a and 4b. By 2013 there will be 15 platforms.

78 Five: two Readings, two Reading Abbeys, and a Reading Evening Post.

79 Puntfield, about one-third of the way to Newbury on the Bath Road.

80 A3290. Vegetation serves as a crash barrier.

81 Nice to Stranraer, by way of Mulhouse, Antwerp, London and Hawick; the path is intended to continue through Ireland to Galway.

82 3¾ minutes. Thomas Cook's European Timetable tells us that all stations in Russia still use Moscow time, including Kaliningrad where local time is one hour behind.

WATER

83 The Holy Brook.

84 Five: Caversham, Blake's, County, Southcote and Fobney.

85 It controls boats through the Oracle and the cramped High Bridge

86 1957; it was then Soundy's Mill.

87 The Loddon Lily, *Leucojum aestivum*. The best place to see them is by the towpath off the end of Willow Lane, Wargrave.

88 The Holy Brook culvert south of Castle Street. It is partly made of ex-Abbey stonework, some of it carved.

89 The Kennet, at Fobney waterworks. Until 1900 water was drawn off somewhere near the Oracle.

90 Islands in the Thames in and around Reading. No-one knows why the Elephants' Graveyard, by Christchurch Meadows, is so called.

WHERE IS IT?

91 St James's church

92 St Laurence's church

93 St Mary's church

94 St Mary's, Castle Street

95 Greyfriars church

96 Queen's Road car park

97 Chatham Place car park

98 Broad Street Mall car park

99 Wesley church

100 Christchurch

101 St Giles's church

102 Battle Library

103 Grovelands church

104 Orthodox Synagogue

105 Caversham Library

106 Oxford Road Mosque

107 Caversham Court gazebo

108 Abbey Gateway

109 Reading Gaol

110 Town Hall

Two Rivers Press has been publishing in and about Reading since 1994. Founded by the artist Peter Hay (1951–2003), the press continues to delight readers, local and further afield, with its varied list of individually designed, thought-provoking books.